RUTH BROWN

A Gallery of Cats

Scallywag Press Ltd

For Tom –

who wandered into a side room whilst visiting
an art gallery with his granny, and found himself
in a very different exhibition indeed . . .

"Wow!" said Tom. His voice echoed in the emptiness as he read aloud from the label next to the painting.

"**JACKSON**
(American Wirehair)
Adventurous and curious . . .
but messy —
often scattering the contents
of his food bowl and litter tray
all over the floor."

Tom wondered where Jackson was going . . .

He read out the next label.

"GUSTAV
(Exotic / Persian cross)
When his home was destroyed
his pampered lifestyle ended.
Despite keeping his air of superiority,
he is friendly and sociable."

Then Tom looked down.
Sitting right in front of him
was Jackson.

"Hello," said Tom, surprised.
"Are you going to introduce
me to your friends?
You show me the way and
I'll read you the labels."

And that is what they did, all the way through the gallery . . .

"**PIET**
(Black and white)
Straightforward and uncomplicated.
He was found, abandoned,
shut inside a large cardboard box."

"Well, at least he can escape now,"
said Tom.

PIET
(Black and white)
Straightforward and uncomplicated.
He was found, abandoned,
shut inside a large cardboard box.

"FRIDA
(Exotic / Spanish wildcat cross)
Slightly lame due to a past accident,
yet independent and full of life.
Sometimes fiery,
sometimes temperamental,
but always affectionate."

"RENÉ
(Chartreux)
A gentle dreamer.
Perfectly happy to sit and stare
at the moon,
or the wall or, indeed, nothing at all.
But not at water."

Ceci n'est pas un chat.

"**VINCENT**
(Ginger / feral)
Totally unpredictable.
Aggressive,
watchful,
occasionally sociable,
but happiest out in the fields
chasing crows."

"MAUKIE & CORNELIS
(Short-haired White)
Two sides of the same coin
who complement each other
in all respects.
Sometimes find the world
puzzling."

MAUKIE & CORNELIS
(Short-haired White)
Two sides of the same coin
who complement each other
in all respects.
Sometimes find the world
puzzling.

"**KATS**
(Japanese bobtail)
He is old now
and rarely leaves his bed,
so can only dream of past travels
and adventures."

"**HENRI**
(Munchkin)
Nicknamed 'Petit Bijou'.
Found in an alley
with the feral cats,
who accepted him
despite his unusual appearance."

"EDVARD
(Norwegian Forest cat)
Nervous
and easily spooked.
Should live as
a house cat,
in a quiet home
with a quiet old lady."

"I wonder if Granny would like him,"
thought Tom.

EDVARD
(Norwegian Forest cat)
Nervous
and easily spooked.
Should live as
a house cat,
in a quiet home
with a quiet old lady.

"WILLIAM
(Persian kitten)
Loves chasing butterflies,
wherever he can find them.
Not always useful as a result,
but beautiful,
so deserving of a place
in anybody's home."

WILLIAM
(Persian kitten)
Loves chasing butterflies,
wherever he can find them.
Not always useful as a result,
but beautiful,
so deserving of a place
in anybody's home.

"SAMUEL
(English Tabby)
Loves nothing more
than to sit in the wilderness,
waiting for hours and hours
to capture whatever comes into view."

SAMUEL
(English Tabby)
Loves nothing more
than to sit in the wilderness,
waiting for hours and hours
to capture whatever comes into view.

By now, there were so many cats milling
about his feet, Tom wasn't sure
what to do with them.

Then they turned a corner . . .

"I suppose this cat just RROOOAAAARRS," Tom laughed. But the cats had already turned and fled, back to the safety of their paintings . . .

All except Jackson, who waited to say goodbye.